2007

Mini Saga Competition

Young Writers

in association with

STAEDTLER

mini S·A·G·A·S·

West Country

First published in Great Britain in 2007 by
Young Writers, Remus House, Coltsfoot Drive,
Peterborough, PE2 9JX
Tel (01733) 890066 Fax (01733) 313524
All Rights Reserved

Foreword

Young Writers was established in 1991, with the aim of encouraging the children and young adults of today to think and write creatively. Our latest secondary school competition, 'Mini S.A.G.A.S.', posed an exciting challenge for these young authors: to write, in no more than fifty words, a story encompassing a beginning, a middle and an end. We call this the mini saga.

Mini S.A.G.A.S. West Country is our latest offering from the wealth of young talent that has mastered this incredibly challenging form. With such an abundance of imagination, humour and ability evident in such a wide variety of stories, these young writers cannot fail to enthral and excite with every tale.

Contents

Downside School, Radstock

Worle School, Weston-Super-Mare

The Mini Sagas

The End Of The Line

The end of the line, my heart frozen in fear. There pointing that cursed blade, risen above my face. Tears bleeding down my skin, stood over me, shadowing me with that etching silhouette, the last thing dancing in my mind was my mother smiling down on me, smiling, pleasantly there.

Anthony Hall (15)
Bishops' College, Gloucester

Cold Heart

My heart ran cold of blood and I could hear muffled
screams. My sight went blurred and my knees
buckled. Although my body collapsed I could feel
myself rise slowly, I could feel myself separate. The
wind wisped straight through me and I was free in
my own world: dead.

Edward Winter (15)
Bishops' College, Gloucester

14

Dreams Do Come True

I thundered down the pitch with the ball at my feet. The tackles were coming at me thick and fast. I had just got past the last two defenders. All I had left to beat was the goalie. One on one, me and him, I had a shot. I scored!

Paige Gough (13)
Bishops' College, Gloucester

15

The Buzzing Sound

Buzzz. I switch it on. *Buzzz* it goes again. The vibration on the floor travels to my feet. I hear the sound again. I kneel on the floor and move with the sound. Forward, forward, forward, then the sound just freezes. I look up and it is the loud computer!

Emily Reed (13)
Bishops' College, Gloucester

What I Love At Christmas

The wrapper rustled like the frosty leaves in the winter breeze. Being careful not to break it because it would ruin the red and white stripy pattern. The colours reminded me of the Christmas season. The red like Santa's suit and the white like the snow. *I love candy canes!*

Jade Presley (13)
Bishops' College, Gloucester

My Dreamy Forest Walk

I'm running through the forest. Am I dreaming? I
don't think so. I'm crying but why? Is it sadness or
joy? Who knows? I want to be free. I want to fly
away! To live by the laws of nature. I hear footsteps.
A yell. I wake up. Damn it!

Hannah Barton (12)
Bishops' College, Gloucester

18

The Climb

I climbed up and up, pursued by the only person I trusted, trying to dodge the gunshots without success. I got to the top. As I was resting from my numerous wounds I saw her. She came up to me, suddenly her face changed, and I fell to eternal rest.

Felix Martin (13)
Bishops' College, Gloucester

19

Paper Round

Squeak, as I pulled the brakes on when I rolled up the drive.
The letter box banged as I pushed the damp daily paper through, the irritating noise of my waterproof trousers rubbing together as I peddled down the road.
I rode away in the rain, not looking back.

Joe Gamston (15)
Bishops' College, Gloucester

20

The Little Lost Sister!

There were two princesses in the land of Daglad.
They never got on but never forgot each other.
One of the princesses got kidnapped; she was on
the planet of Zargor, their feared enemy. The other
princess went on a voyage after her sister. In the end
she found her.

Georgia Morris (13)
Bishops' College, Gloucester

The Entire Drift

Kzzz, the noise of the dongvelve whilst changing gear, hitting on the handbrake whilst turning the wheel, hearing the tyres screech, letting go of the handbrake and straightening the car back up, this is an entire drift. I can hear the car behind me losing control. I have won … again.

Samuel Etheridge (13)

Bishops' College, Gloucester

22

Heartbroken

As he lies there with his corpse-white lips and pale cold face, a tear drops from my brown eye. I place a rosy red rose upon his cold heart. I turn and say goodbye, as I can't face any more. My heart is broken more than it has before.

Roni Vizor (13)
Bishops' College, Gloucester

23

I Want To Be Famous

Hi I'm Jim and I want to be famous. I'm not very talented so I can't sing or act. I'm just very fast, so I started racing, I'm really good because I train. I have a motive *run fast* … because the neighbour's dog is big and stones make dogs angry!

Brandon Westcarr (13)
Bishops' College, Gloucester

Men, Babies And Grief

It all seemed too good to be true at the beginning.
Then they came and took my true love away from
me. Spencer was an ex-con; he had only been out
nine months. We were happy. I was having his baby.
But those terrible men took his life away.

Hannah Davis (14)
Bishops' College, Gloucester

Driftah

The tyres smoked. Around the corner as I pulled the handbrake. The back end slid out and then the sirens turned on as the corner finished so my foot slammed to the floor, smoke poured from the wheels. I could see the blue lights flashing then *bang!* My end. Tyres popped.

Kyle Pope (13)
Bishops' College, Gloucester

The Thing

It was dark out, there was a full moon and I had to walk through the woods to get home from school. I heard a rustling. I stopped and looked around. I saw something move. I ran. Then it was in front of me. Then I woke, it wasn't real.

Tommy Davis (11)
Bishops' College, Gloucester

The Thing

Oh no it's getting closer and closer. Just keep running,
I thought. I could feel its cold breath on my neck. I
stopped. I turned, 'Argh! Help!' I screamed.
'Please stop screaming, you dropped your phone on
the side of the road, I thought I should return it to
you!'

Phillip Turner (12)
Bishops' College, Gloucester

28

Premonition

I saw my death. Flames were licking at my broken body, lifting it up with its stinging hands. My body turned lifeless, my hair alight, a replica of a Hell-born Medusa. The bright sparks laughed at my emotionless face, mocking me, I awoke. Then the oven charged - on fire.

Ieashia Hamlin (12)
Bishops' College, Gloucester

Dance

I came out of my room in my sparkly costume. I gazed at all of the other kids around me. I glared into the crowd as I noticed my mum and dad crying with pride. I climbed up on the stage waiting for my music to play. And I danced.

Sophie Clack (14)
Bishops' College, Gloucester

The Room

The noise got louder and louder as I went closer to the empty room in the huge house. I opened the door, the door squeaked and the floor creaked, as I stepped inside the room was dark, quiet. All I could hear was my own breath and then I fainted.

Mohibul Alam (12)
Bishops' College, Gloucester

Chaverella And The Hairy Gothmother

Once there lived a princess called Chaverella who hated Goths. One day a woman popped up and said hello.

'Who are you?' asked Chaverella.

'I am the hairy gothmother and I have come to get you!'

'Why?' asked Chaverella.

'Because you hate me.'

Zap and Chaverella disappeared!

Martin Sysum (14)

Bishops' College, Gloucester

32

Missing Cat

Rousing up, the sun glistened on my sparkling eyes. I noticed I'd lost my cat that cuddled himself in his bed.
One sunlit day, I saw my cat creeping behind this man, an odd man who looked queasy. Falling in love, I chose that life, but my father slaughtered him.

Mithura Manoharan (14)
Bishops' College, Gloucester

Pirate Ship

I was flying from side to side, very high up. I felt like I was going to fall out. I was strapped in by only a thin bar. Suddenly, I slipped out of the side. I could hear screaming, it was too late. I was on the floor - in pieces.

Lauren Williams (12)
Cheltenham Kingsmead School, Cheltenham

Bob's Escape

No movement, he was on his back. I used a net to
pick him up. Poor Bob. He only lasted a month. I
should have fed him. *Plop!* In the water, pull the flush.
He woke up. *Stop!*
Too late he's free.

James Russ-Charman (12)
Cheltenham Kingsmead School, Cheltenham

35

Green Street

'I'm forever blowing bubbles, pretty bubbles in the
air.'
That's all you can hear, Hammer fans going mental.
All chanting, 'GSE, GSE.' They're going mad, as their
team have scored.
Later, the West Brom fans walk into the pub, it all
falls silent, the fight begins.

Ryan Payne (12)
Cheltenham Kingsmead School, Cheltenham

Will He Or Won't He?

He stood at the bottom of the mountain with five words on his mind. *Will I or won't I?* He climbed up the mountain, still with the words on his mind. *Will I or won't I?* He stood at the edge, peering down. Will he or won't he?

Sophie Kennedy (12)
Cheltenham Kingsmead School, Cheltenham

Patrol

My day started when I went to work. I am police patrol. I was the best in town. Until today. I was called out to a person who was going to jump off a building. I tried everything to stop him but he jumped. Will this hell ever end?

Matthew Hopkins
Cheltenham Kingsmead School, Cheltenham

The House Of Doom

They call you in; you walk into a small, crowded
room. You stay there until a door opens. It leads
you into a bigger room. Darkness. A strange voice
speaks. That's all you can hear. The lights come back
on. Leading you through a door and into the gift
shop.

Aaron Holmes (12)
Cheltenham Kingsmead School, Cheltenham

39

The Thing!

Sat on the side, swinging my legs, slowly a long dark
object appeared in the water. I slipped into the water
and my goggles fell half on my eyes, closing them
shut. Shouting, 'Help! This thing's taking chunks out
of me!' *Beware The Thing*' the sign said. Too late now

. . .

Sarah Gunston (12)
Cheltenham Kingsmead School, Cheltenham

40

Blue Ogre

In a swamp far away a blue, fat ogre lived. He was on a quest to save a donkey. Donkey was in a stable at the top of a mountain.
As the ogre got to the stable, Donkey was asleep so the ogre had to carry Donkey to the bottom.

Richard Fry (12)
Cheltenham Kingsmead School, Cheltenham

41

Nerves And Wood

I held the wood in front of me, just a strap holding it close to me. I held a piece of plastic in the other hand. I heard the crowd enter and scream, suddenly little metal snakes came around me. They stopped then returned to the string of my guitar.

Amy Beff (12)
Cheltenham Kingsmead School, Cheltenham

Hallowe'en

A castle, dark and stormy by night, zombies, ghosts
and wolves.
By day to die for. A beautiful family home.
The first Hallowe'en.
The freaks step out to stalk their prey.
Daybreak – the beautiful family home, the scene of a
macabre massacre.

Jack Edmondson (12)
Chipping Campden School, Chipping Campden

Panic

Panic reigns as the siren sounds. The streets clear
almost instantly.
'Incoming!'
Boom!
'Is anyone hurt?'
No response.
'Is anyone hurt?'
Everyone's dead.
Total devastation.

Joe Clufey (12)
Chipping Campden School, Chipping Campden

Untitled

It's Sunday, me and my best friend are walking along a cliff. I lean on the fencing to shout my name. Suddenly I am falling. I can't even hear my best friend screaming.
I wake up in a cold sweat screaming my last words.

Grace Taylor (12)
Chipping Campden School, Chipping Campden

45

My Car

My car has leopard print seats and radiant flashing lights; it's the latest fashion. It automatically locates sweet shops; the seats fold up into giant beds and it drives on water. It has a 1,000-watt stereo and self-filling fridge. I love my car.
'John, you're late for school!'

Megan Barry (11)
Chipping Campden School, Chipping Campden

Fox

One day I was eating some grass when I heard the clopping of horses' hooves. I turned round and it was the north Cotswold hunt trying to kill me! I ran but the hounds noticed me and chased after me. I went down a hole. And then I got away.

Franky Johnson (12)
Chipping Campden School, Chipping Campden

The Zoo

It walks slowly along the fresh laid tarmac, everyone
scared, watching his every step. People screaming …
people shouting. Pointing and running.
It turns, roars, 'What's wrong?' It just gets screamed
at!
Bang! Bang!
'Get up Bob, you're gonna miss your bus!'

Edward Adams (12)
Chipping Campden School, Chipping Campden

48

The Golden Eye

The mysterious teacher stamps through the chaotic corridor growling at anyone in his path. He wears an eyepatch. Detention. Someone was waiting, he heard rumours that if you have detention with the teacher with the eyepatch you disappear.
Inside the teacher revealed his golden eye.

Michael Hancock (12)
Chipping Campden School, Chipping Campden

A Huge Step

I walked through the gates and stepped into a new world, one that I hadn't come across before. It was like transforming from a goldfish in a puddle to a goldfish in a lake. New faces, new places. It seemed so scary but I really enjoy it now.

Isobel Skarratt (12)

Chipping Campden School, Chipping Campden

The Lonely Caravan

The wolf howled up at the moon in the silent night.
The caravan trundled past; the head guard drew his
sword as he heard the cloud screech above him. A
shadow fell over the guards. *'Argh!'*
They disappeared one by one as the cloud covered
them.

Josh McQuail (12)
Chipping Campden School, Chipping Campden

The Chase

My paws hit the ground softly as I creep around the garden. Suddenly I see bright colours in the sky. I pounce, I miss, I try again, no luck. It dodges out my way for the last time. The butterfly gets away.

Catharine Cromack (12)

Chipping Campden School, Chipping Campden

No Turning Back

I kept falling. All I could think was why? Why the hell did I jump? I knew I couldn't fly. This was the most selfish thing I had ever done. My life flashed before my eyes. We used to be best friends. What had happened? I couldn't turn back now …

Charli Parsons
Chipping Campden School, Chipping Campden

Never-Ending Road

Breathing heavily, legs aching, looking for a place to hide. I turn around, nothing. Gone. But where? I don't stop though, it might catch up. I run and run down an endless road hoping to find an exit to this place.
I sit up, it was a dream.

Emily Gibbard
Chipping Campden School, Chipping Campden

It's Raining

The rain is pouring; cutting down like a knife. It's been hours, days, years - and it's not going. The world's moved on: but I haven't. The sky is blue and the sun is shining but it's raining inside.

Alice Preston-Jones
Chipping Campden School, Chipping Campden

Untitled

She screamed. My heart skipped a beat. I was so frightened, it took me at least a while to realise she was screaming over a spider. The big crawly, 8-legged monster ran across the room. She screamed. I screamed. We both jumped on a chair and laughed.

Louisa Ryan
Chipping Campden School, Chipping Campden

Foxes

There are two foxes. There are two men. There are two horses. There are two dogs. There are two guns. There are no foxes. The fox was only living its life to kill a few of the millions of rabbits for food. Yet the humans killed the foxes for fun.

Max Brambani

Chipping Campden School, Chipping Campden

The Box

What evil could be contained inside this innocent container? Terrors and horrific images had been imprisoned inside for eternity. Yet it had been bestowed upon me to open this Pandora's box of suffering. Eyes shut I opened it. Nothing. I opened my eyes, peered into the box to see … socks.

Alice Bennett
Chipping Campden School, Chipping Campden

Him

I saw him walk past me, he does the same every day, and he never notices me. Not even a look. I stare, willing him to look in my direction. Suddenly I shout his name. I don't know what possessed me. The words just fell out of my mouth!

Emma Easter
Chipping Campden School, Chipping Campden

Questing

Trees came crushing down in the great forest, as a noble knight strode forward upon the finest of stallions. A great mythical dragon was his quest set. He entered the damp and dingy cave; the floor littered with jewels the size of your head, coins as shiny as the sun.

Alexander Isles
Chipping Campden School, Chipping Campden

Escape?

Racing through thin arms of wood with voices surrounding every movement. Is it laughter or cries for help?
Breaking through they reach the light, light of daylight and freedom. To the fence for no one to escape, children going in, can they go out?
Climb over and reach … the playground.

Megan Hartneff
Chipping Campden School, Chipping Campden

Eww!

I watched in horror, as I witnessed something that no one should ever, ever have to see, and I mean it. My stomach churned, I felt unclean and disgusted. My sister and, I can't even say it, her boyfriend, lips and slobber. I gritted my teeth and closed my eyes.

Anna-Sophia Menato
Chipping Campden School, Chipping Campden

Untitled

She screamed in pain as she saw the sword drawn above her. He merely laughed. She screamed some more. He merely covered her mouth. The sword was drawn back in line with her head and she began to cry. Just as he struck Mum screamed,' Kids it's time for tea!'

Bethan Ripley

Chipping Campden School, Chipping Campden

63

Midnight

Tick-tock. Shadows dance like agile pixies, around the room. Paralysed by fear, I lie motionless, eyes wide, glassy, glazed over. My heart leaps into my throat and makes me gag at every creak. The clock deafeningly declares the midnight hour, and my eyelids fall, heavy as lead, insomnia surrenders.

Lily Smith
Chipping Campden School, Chipping Campden

64

Hostage

As I wiped the sweat from my brow, I floated down to the ground, missing shots from the AK47s. I was thinking, the closer I got the easier the shot became. I landed and hid behind the wall. The team followed as we fought through the barricades … Hostage saved!

Craig Robins

Chipping Campden School, Chipping Campden

Untitled.

Three words. Three words that could save me for one more night. But no, people are too self-centred to give me the contents of one of their pockets. They wouldn't spit on me even if I were on fire. They don't care about me.

'Any spare change please sir?'

Alice Youds
Chipping Campden School, Chipping Campden

The Race

Racing the birds. Wind in my face, watching the world go by. Sweating, steaming, hoping to win, close to the end, running out of time. I'm across the line!
I've won!
Slowing down, stopping, pulse racing, breathing heavy …
I wake up, lay in bed, it was all a dream.

Danyel Watson
Chipping Campden School, Chipping Campden

Untitled

Running through this deep, dark alley. My breath
becoming shorter and shorter. I turn to face it, my
eyes clamped open in fear. I stumble over in my haste
with its jaws closing down on me. What can I do?
There's no escape now!
False alarm, it's just the cat!

Fred Nott
Chipping Campden School, Chipping Campden

Someone's Watching Me!

I feel eyes in the back of my neck, footsteps heavily hitting the floor and the street full of eerie-looking shadows. I start to run, not looking back, as fast as I can. I'm scared. A hand grabs my shoulder. I turn to find my friends laughing at me.

Kathy-May Smith

Chipping Campden School, Chipping Campden

Amazing

Lights flashed. It was amazing, the adrenalin rush that came over me. All this was blowing in my face. Music blaring out into my ears, the world spinning madly. I just had to pay another three pounds, to go on the Waltzers again. It was just the most amazing ride!

Dennise Gibson
Chipping Campden School, Chipping Campden

Nothing

Her face a pale white, her tears rolling down her
cheeks, her body sat in a puddle … her fingers
pointing behind me … I turn around …
Bodies lying all over the road and pavement …
One car …
Upside down …
No screaming,
Nothing;
Just silence.

Megan Clufey

Chipping Campden School, Chipping Campden

Never Ever

How harmful can a shopping trip to Tesco be? For me. Terrible. Got in the car, drove up the big hill to Tescos, me and Mum did our shop.
Got to the car, reached the hill, we couldn't slow down, faster and faster. At the end, *smash!* we're dead.

Tom Jones
Chipping Campden School, Chipping Campden

Dragons, Fire, Teeth . . .

My heart is throbbing, legs trembling, hands shaking
but my ancient blade is standing strong … Dash!
Evade! Stab! Missed! Darn it … Lucky I'm fireproof
but I'm not bite-proof!

Jonathan Musgrove
Chipping Campden School, Chipping Campden

73

Untitled

He never noticed his broken mirror.
He never noticed the black cat on his way to work.
He never stopped to think about walking under that
cleaner's ladder.
He never saw that man with two hands outstretched,
holding a gun ...
All he was, was blind.

Ben Ormshaw
Chipping Campden School, Chipping Campden

74

Burning Towers

Out of the taxi. Time for a donut and coffee? Maybe not. Then again … OK but quickly.
There we go. Much better. So, to work I guess. Out of the coffee shop but it's dark. Much darker, clouds of dust and smoke. The towers, they're burning.

Peter Rycroft

Chipping Campden School, Chipping Campden

Waiting For Ray

My brother Ray always wanted to be in the army. He went last week. His room is the same except he isn't there. I watch the news every day and hear about the fighting. I feel warm tears run down my cheeks. No news. Still here, still waiting for Ray …

Emma Bennett (14)
Chipping Sodbury School, Chipping Sodbury

Captain Codman And The Terror Of The Falling Builder

Captain Codman was having a swim when suddenly someone was in danger. He jumped out of the swimming pool and flew through the roof to try and find the person that was in danger. He saw a builder hanging off a skyscraper. Codman swooped up and took him down.

Michael Bamford (11)
Chipping Sodbury School, Chipping Sodbury

77

Demon Cave

Casat found a dragon egg and took it home. Casat raised it to be a mighty dragon. They flew to Demon Cave. Casat had his sword at his waist. They entered and saw a pair of glowing red eyes. He charged at it, drew his sword and slaughtered the beast.

Nathan Woolfrey (12)
Chipping Sodbury School, Chipping Sodbury

School Creeps

At 12pm I went into the school, I heard a slap and a bang then wondered what it was. Creeping quietly not making a noise I tried to figure it out. I thought it was a ghost haunting the school once more. Then I heard the noise again!

Hannah Rendall (11)
Chipping Sodbury School, Chipping Sodbury

Drag Driver

There was a rookie drag driver that came from England with his family to Switzerland. Straight away he came across the drag king. The rookie joined a rich man's car club. From then on he got a new car and out skilled the drag king therefore claiming his title.

Gregory Hiff (12)
Chipping Sodbury School, Chipping Sodbury

Mission Andy

Matt was on a mission to kill, he was an assassin. He had to kill Andy, manager of a huge bank, the Abacus. It was all going to plan, but suddenly out of nowhere popped up Andaca (the evil three-legged monster). Matt shot, shot Andy. The bank manager died!

Rob Belcher (12)

Chipping Sodbury School, Chipping Sodbury

School

Two girls, late for school one day, had to go to the
head teacher's office to get the cane.
'I'm not going to get the cane,' one said. She went to
find a demon instead. The door locked behind her!
'Is it too late to have the cane instead?'

Sophie Talbot (12)
Chipping Sodbury School, Chipping Sodbury

Horror In School

There was a haunted school in a field. One night three children went to the school as a dare. They entered the school. There was a huge hole in the floor that they all fell down. Parents wondered where they were.
Thirteen years later they appeared …

Alex McMillan (12)
Chipping Sodbury School, Chipping Sodbury

Hallowe'en Horror

It was Hallowe'en and Chipping Sodbury School
were organising parties. They made a dunking game,
but instead of using water they used petrol.
The time had come and everyone was arriving.
Someone dunked their head in and got an apple.
'My face is burning somebody call an ambulance!'

Sammie Coles (12)
Chipping Sodbury School, Chipping Sodbury

Unknown Face

A young girl was going into a shop when someone grabbed her. They took her away and said, 'We have been waiting for you.' The place she was in she recognised but she did not know where from. 'Do you remember me?' he asked. Who was he? She didn't know.

Kelly Murray (12)
Chipping Sodbury School, Chipping Sodbury

Chloe And The Zoo Garden

One night as Chloe slept, she thought she could hear animal noises coming from her garden. She slipped out of bed, peered out of her window and, to her amazement; the garden was full of animals! 'Good morning!' whispered her mum and suddenly Chloe realised it was all a dream.

Harriet Dean (12)
Chipping Sodbury School, Chipping Sodbury

The Ghostly Castle!

Andrea and Tom went to a castle. People said it was haunted. They climbed through the window. The alarm went off, Tom got caught in a cage. Andrea ran. Ghosts were following her. It was dark so she pulled a blind open.

The ghosts died from the brightness. *Phew!*

Keeana Hall (11)
Chipping Sodbury School, Chipping Sodbury

The Martian Race Reborn

On Mars, two astronauts find a remnant of Martian history. These astronauts are Fred and Jane. The remnant is found in a crater up north of the planet. There is a hole the same size, which the astronauts put the remnant in. A nearby crater opens, the Martians are reborn.

Thomas Evans (12)
Chipping Sodbury School, Chipping Sodbury

Captain Cap Man, The Rise Of The Titanium Fist

Our family went to Capland. An evil villain, named the Titanium Fist, started to cause masses of destruction. From one of the stands flew a hat. As it hit me, I turned into Captain Cap Man. I took a manhole cover and threw it. It hit him, he fell, dead.

Matthew Abley (11)
Chipping Sodbury School, Chipping Sodbury

Forever Running

Running through the field, sweat dripped down my face, a gang of people chased me. They were waiting in the woods. I ran to the top and jumped onto the path. They were still chasing me. I jumped into the river. I lost them. I made it to the shops.

Ben Batey (14)
Chipping Sodbury School, Chipping Sodbury

The Secret Princess

There was a little girl. The day before her 12th birthday she went for a walk in the forest. She found a big pink castle and found out she was a princess. 'This is the best birthday ever!' said the little girl. Then she lived happily ever after.

Lizi Cox (14)

Chipping Sodbury School, Chipping Sodbury

The Fairy Princess

Fairy Princess Alanna is left with her greedy father Raymond as her mother died. She gets lonely as no friends are there for her to talk to. She says, 'How I wish I was an ordinary girl and had many friends.' She sneaks out and runs away to another land.

Lauren Prentice (14)
Chipping Sodbury School, Chipping Sodbury

The Rescue

Mervin was back. My sisters had gone. That was the last straw. I left my grandmother in search of my family. I was searching for ages before I saw the castle across the river. I crossed the river and rescued my family. Me and my family made it back safely.

George Rumble (14)

Chipping Sodbury School, Chipping Sodbury

Link

Link is an unworthy knight on a journey to rescue a princess. He goes through horrific challenges to reach the love of his life. Link reaches his destination and lays his eyes on her! Link asks for her hand.
'I do,' she says.
'My dreams have come true!' exclaims Link.

Chelsey Whittingham (14)
Chipping Sodbury School, Chipping Sodbury

The Princess And The Dwarf

Dwarf Harry reads about Princess Maria. He goes to rescue her from the smallest room of the tallest tower. He has to fight the giants, trolls and dragon. She doesn't want to marry him because he's a dwarf but then she realises it doesn't matter. They live happily ever after.

Kelly Provis (14)

Chipping Sodbury School, Chipping Sodbury

The Pinky Star

'The Pinky Star' is a bright bubblegum-pink café.
Everything down to the last atom is pink!
One day a box appeared. Inside was a key and note.
The staff followed on a quest and found the Pinky
Star! The café had found the star and turned the
world pink!

Stephanie Cook (14)
Chipping Sodbury School, Chipping Sodbury

Ten Year Coma

'Come back here. I need ten grand.'
Running, car coming, it hits me, *bang!*
'Where am I? What do you want?'
'Calm down.'
'No must get out of here!'
Hover cars, skateboards, where am I? 'Help me!' I
see the newspaper. It says 2017 but it's 2007!

Sam Haff (13)

Chipping Sodbury School, Chipping Sodbury

97

Misunderstood?

She stood, trembling all over. There was silence. Her mind was blank, tears streamed down her face. She gazed down at the frozen corpse and her blood-drenched dress. She collapsed.
Hours later she woke. The handcuffs rubbed her wrists. She was caught.

Maria De Freitas (13)
Chipping Sodbury School, Chipping Sodbury

98

Cream-Cake Crash

It came round turn 6 slowly, but broke away from its competitor at the pit straight with fantastic acceleration. He entered the first hairpin, speed dropped, his eye caught the race leader's hover car soaring over the barrier. Cream Cake 2 was finished. Jim woke in a puddle of sweat.

James Affington (13)
Chipping Sodbury School, Chipping Sodbury

Walking Through School

People were laughing, pointing in my direction, whispering behind hands. I started walking faster. Then I found out I had a note on my back, anxiously I looked: 'What's the difference between a boring teacher and a boring book? You can shut the book up'!

Shannie Haff (13)

Chipping Sodbury School, Chipping Sodbury

The Clearing

Kameno stood in the clearing of trees, the luscious colours bearing down on him. He flapped his wings and peered over the treetops, looking ahead at the war raging on the hilltop. He couldn't help thinking, *did I start this?*
He hovered back down and slept long into the night.

Daniel Jones (12)
Chipping Sodbury School, Chipping Sodbury

Bump In The Night

Flash! The lightning, *crash!* The thunder. He was
hiding under the bed.
'Anybody home?'
A rattle downstairs followed by a horrible scream.
He crept downstairs quaking in his slippers. He found
Dad holding his head.
'I bumped my head in the night!'

Liam Towiffs (13)
Chipping Sodbury School, Chipping Sodbury

School

It was a Friday. A science teacher was marking some work. Suddenly a man stabbed him from behind. The weekend passed. Another teacher came in and saw him … *dead*. The teacher screamed.
The head teacher questioned all the teachers but it was one of the students …

Laura Daniels (12)
Chipping Sodbury School, Chipping Sodbury

Valley Of Death

This story is about a valley of dead people lying everywhere hanging from the walls, stuck to the floor. You go in and you will never be seen again. I know this because I once saw a whole army of people flash and die in a matter of seconds.

Joseph Garrett (12)
Chipping Sodbury School, Chipping Sodbury

Love At First Sight!

Walking along the grass, my best gown flowing! I bumped into a boy, the most handsome boy I'd ever seen! He asked my name, I asked his. 'Prince Charming.'
I replied, 'My mother always said I'd find you!'
It was love at first sight! We went hand in hand.

Jessica Cheape (14)
Churchdown School, Gloucester

Murder

A cat observed. It was quick. Painless. The silencer on the end of the barrel ensured no one was aware. No one but the cat. It saw it all. Of course he didn't understand. Why would he understand what took place? All alone, unable to tell. The sole, unknowing eyewitness.

Kieran Toft (14)
Churchdown School, Gloucester

Who's There?

A knock at the door sprung me to my feet. I opened the decrepit door, no one was there. I shut the door and it banged again. I hesitated, should I open it? I slowly edged towards the handle, it creaked as it opened, the milkman.
'Oh hello there love!'

Holly Reynolds (14)
Churchdown School, Gloucester

107

A Summer's Day

On a hot summer's day we went for a picnic in the local park. We all sat under a large blossomed tree beside the flowing brook. Mum was sunbathing and reading her book and I was playing frisbee with my dad. It started to get chilly so we went home.

Emma Price (14)
Churchdown School, Gloucester

Early Dinner

One day a boy was walking to the shop to buy dinner when he saw a crocodile on the road. The boy tried to dodge it but it ferociously snapped its jaws and crept up to the boy. He tried to escape, but the crocodile snaffled him up for dinner!

Hannah Doran (14)
Churchdown School, Gloucester

Ghosts

One day as I went to get in bed I saw something.
Was it a ghost? No it couldn't be they don't exist, or
do they?
The next day I saw it again. It must be a ghost …
tomorrow I will investigate!

Emma Shorter (12)
Cirencester Kingshill School, Cirencester

Drums

Jamie Carter was a normal man with a normal job. He was walking down a back alley when he was snatched. Drums started and he was told to roll some dice, Jamie was very scared, they were all pointing guns at him. He rolled and the drums stopped. 6,6.

Alex Pinnock (12)

Cirencester Kingshill School, Cirencester

Untitled

One stormy night I was looking out my window and saw a man with a hook for a hand. He started knocking on my door. I ran downstairs but my mum was already brutally murdered.
I ran outside but there was no one within a mile. I was terrified.

Joe Tye
Cirencester Kingshill School, Cirencester

The Creepy House

It was dull. The rain was pouring down. Suddenly, I heard someone calling for help. I looked back, no one was there. Standing there, was a creepy house. I went up to the creepy house. There stood a girl. The door opened. I stepped in. I tried to get out …

Mereoni Wara (12)
Cirencester Kingshill School, Cirencester

The Cove

I told him not to go near the Devil's cove, but he insisted he went to look for our sister. He went at the start of the year. We waited for days, then weeks, months and finally a year but my dear brother never came home.

Samuel Johnson (12)
Cirencester Kingshill School, Cirencester

What Was It?

Early one morning I was walking my dog down the road, going to the park when I realised there was something staring at me. It was black all over and it started hissing. It turned a bit more so it was looking me directly in the eyes, then I ran.

Alice Jones (12)

Cirencester Kingshill School, Cirencester

The Haunted Hotel

There was once a haunted hotel, which was full of ghosts. Phil was going to spend the night there. Phil arrived at the hotel but went straight to bed. He dreamt of ghosts torturing him, he woke up, terrified of his nightmare. But he noticed that his suitcase had disappeared.

Gregory Estaff (12)

Cirencester Kingshill School, Cirencester

The Blur In My Bedroom

This story is from the middle ages.
It was a winter's evening and as I went to bed the
clock struck 12. I leapt in my bed but as I was about
to fall asleep my door swung open and all I can
remember seeing was the blurriest image ever.

Gemma Logan (12)
Cirencester Kingshill School, Cirencester

The Spy

I followed, watching his every move, he entered a warehouse. I lurked in the shadows. He shouted, 'Come out.' I'd been found! He wheeled around with a gun in his hand. The next thing I knew, I was lying on the ground with my warm blood oozing between my fingers.

Daniel Barker (12)
Cirencester Kingshill School, Cirencester

Not Much Memory

The doors flung open, *crash*. I remember seeing blood, then hearing my name. Next I saw fluorescent lights, I heard was the beeping of the machines keeping me alive, ringing in my ears. I couldn't move. I was stuck. I had been in a coma for weeks. Don't remember much!

Toni Mottram (13)
Cirencester Kingshill School, Cirencester

Scared

I walked through the gate, suddenly I felt a jolt so I started to pull back, nothing happened but it just carried on, so I let it be until the moment came when I fell onto the hard floor and winded myself, but I got back on the horse, scared!

Tiffany Cairns (11)
Cirencester Kingshill School, Cirencester

A Close Call!

The bus home from school set off as usual down the lanes. Rain splattered against the windscreen. Suddenly a van appeared from nowhere, brakes squealed then *crunch!* as metal and glass collided. I thumped into the seat in front but was unharmed. We now grip our seats round that bend!

Henry Turner (11)
Cirencester Kingshill School, Cirencester

121

Killing Stalker

I thought I was being followed ever since I left my house. The only other person on the street was an old woman, every time I looked back she smiled but not this time, she lay there dead. As the killer approached me, I quickly ran, but it caught me.

Katie Payne (12)
Cirencester Kingshill School, Cirencester

My Family

My family, there's Mum, pop star, sings in shower.
Dad, model parades in his boxers. Sister, queen and
I'm her servant. Brother, fish, swims in pond. Nan,
stuntman, tries riding backwards on motorcycle.
Grandad, entertainer, tells rubbish jokes at dinner.
Me, normal, well I like to think so. My family!

Laura Lewis (12)
Cirencester Kingshill School, Cirencester

Game Over

I'm running, it's chasing, I scream. I stumble. Running
and running, never stop. So scared, I trip and fall on
a tree root. I see the monster's ugly face. The words
game over flash across the screen. I've lost on level 1.
Turn the Xbox back on and try again.

Gina Lewis (12)
Cirencester Kingshill School, Cirencester

Splat

'Aarrgghh! It's after me. *Leave me alone*,' she
screamed. 'Hit it with the waffle thing.'
'OK, OK, I'm coming,' said Steve, following Jane as
she ran round like a headless chicken.
'Quick, quick,' she screeched.
'OK, first of all …'
Splat
'Second, it's not a waffle thing … it's a fly swat!'

Connor Coffier (12)
Cirencester Kingshill School, Cirencester

Disappearance Of Sam

Suddenly there was a massive scream from the next room.
'Are you alright?' shouted Lucy.
There was no reply so she ran into the room where Sam was but where was he? There was no sign of him in the room,
Where could he be? thought Lucy very anxiously wondering.

Sophie Curtis (12)

Cirencester Kingshill School, Cirencester

126

The Knight

There I was next to a knight fighting side by side,
my sword-biting in. Then I saw him coming straight
towards me - tall, dark, mysterious and strong. I
screamed.
I was in bed left cold, shaken. There he was, tall,
dark, mysterious and strong.
'Good morning Jake.'
I froze.

Hayden Russell (12)
Cirencester Kingshill School, Cirencester

Empty Clouds

As I stepped through the wintry storm, I could smell
it. The vast smell of death. I knew that it was a
warning. The men jumped out at me and said, 'You
are going to die when you wake up!'
I woke with a start, I saw just empty clouds.

Sophie Russell (12)
Cirencester Kingshill School, Cirencester

My School Day

I woke up, got dressed, had my breakfast then went to school. I got to school, then I started playing footy with my mates. The bell went for lesson time. The lesson started and soon ended. Next lesson started, it was PE, my favourite. We're playing football, *great fun!*

Tom Jehu (12)
Cirencester Kingshill School, Cirencester

Untitled

Ben was sat on a train, the driver beeped his horn.
Ben looked at the track junction, it had been
changed. They were going to crash into another train
if the controller didn't change the track.
Two seconds later, there was a bang, the train was off
the track.

Jonathan McDonald (12)
Cirencester Kingshill School, Cirencester

The Crushing Weight

Head down, whisky in hand, papers on the table. 'Are you ready?' comes a voice. He says nothing. The corrupt man just walked with a drunk and desperate look in his eyes. Gentlemen waiting by the table, he walks past, gun on the floor, silence, gunshot. Silence.

Caffum Parker (12)

Cirencester Kingshill School, Cirencester

131

The Sorcerer

He stood up, tugged the hem of his sumptious robe,
smirked, a tap at his wand, boomed 'Order! I have a
theory.'
Mutters swoop like gannets.
'Concocted through contemplation.'
A strike scorched the ancient rosewood lecturn.
Mystically a hooded figure rose.
'Words have no meaning unless wielded with
conviction.'
Tranquillity.

James O'Leary (13)
Cirencester Kingshill School, Cirencester

Mirror Horror

There are mirrors everywhere, to the left, to the right, before me, behind me, everywhere I look. I run, *bang*, I hit the mirror, *smash*, it goes, but *bang* there is another one behind, I'm stuck, I will never get out, help me, please my worst nightmare has occurred, help.

Charlotte Morris (13)
Cirencester Kingshill School, Cirencester

Sadness

Sad. Depressed. Two things I was. I felt no need to
live, I felt weak and limp, did I want to live?
I laid down, looked up into the night sky. Staring
at the stars in a daze. I was getting weaker, then I
plunged into darkness.

William Stephens (13)
Cirencester Kingshill School, Cirencester

Sky-High

I stared down at the many fields, all different colours below. I shut my eyes and plunged out of the plane. My stomach filled with a butterfly sensation. My eyes went bloodshot as tears dripped down the side of my face, I grasped the toggle and pulled but nothing happened!

Luke Barton (13)
Cirencester Kingshill School, Cirencester

The War

A man was playing paintballing. An army sergeant spotted and offered him a job in the army. The man said yes so he was trained, then went to war. He was getting shot at, suddenly he threw a grenade and everything went silent - they looked up and they had won.

Marcus Rhodes (13)
Cirencester Kingshill School, Cirencester

Dove

Black claws of death chase me, leaving messy prints on my snowy wings. Heavier and heavier is my flight over the glowing horizon as cooling lava settles on my back. I plummet to the ground. People scream, slam doors, run, there's no hope. Vesuvius has erupted, what happened to peace?

Grace Kinsey (13)
Cirencester Kingshill School, Cirencester

Heart Attack

Drifting away into darkness of the girl's blue eyes.
Slowly dreaming of the day before tomorrow. The
nose … the lips, to the toes and the fingertips.
Thinking of what she's done, heart beating as if she's
in love. Tossing, turning, trying to get help!
A heart attack, she's dead!

Daniella Keen (12)
Cirencester Kingshill School, Cirencester

Roller Coaster And Me

A rusty chain took me to the top and then I rocketed down a track, polished by the wheels on the carriages. Loops and tight turns pushed me to the limit. After a few pulse-raising seconds, the brakes slammed me to a stop! The thrill ride was over.

Isaac Herbert (13)
Cirencester Kingshill School, Cirencester

Crash Landing

Something was wrong. We had gained speed. The pilot spoke an urgent message of distress. We were all going to die, falling hundreds of miles per hour straight into the ground. Help …
I woke up. I was alive. There was carnage but we were all going to be OK.

Stuart Evans (13)
Cirencester Kingshill School, Cirencester

140

Running

Ever running, ever fleeing, men chasing him through time. Never stopping, hardly visible, yet always there. He knows fear yet never happiness. Though hope remains. If he can find the guardians, find their temple, he will have a chance. Running, ever running, always fleeing the men who came through time.

James Barry (13)
Cirencester Kingshill School, Cirencester

141

Space

In outer space, there is no air, lots of planets, so
much to discover, so much space for a new planet.
Men go on the moon to look around for new things,
anything. The spark of excitement. Space is a wonder
only a few can go.

John Cornwell (13)
Cirencester Kingshill School, Cirencester

Cinderella-Chavinderella

A wave of a wand, my rags turn to tracksuit, the pumpkin into my ride, bare feet jump into Nike's, the mice into my possey, the grand ball to Club, 12 o'clock, midnight to 4. Prince Charming to my gangsta boo, ugly sisters to mingas! Perfect speech to slang. Innit.

Carrie Bloodworth (13)

Cirencester Kingshill School, Cirencester

Dead

His heart pounded quickly. Thoughts running through his head. Flashing lights made him close his eyes. The sound of a policeman calling through a microphone went through one ear and out the other. Another step! Gasps coming from below. Little faces stared up at him. Then suddenly he jumped!

Tom Gardiner (13)
Cirencester Kingshill School, Cirencester

The Surprise

The deserted planet was in complete darkness. The only source of light came from my torch, however, it was low on batteries. I shone it around and evil fluorescent orange eyes, at least fifty of them, were on me. I panicked. I ran. I fell, they said, 'Hi.'

Dan Mills (13)
Cirencester Kingshill School, Cirencester

Free

As I sat in the bleak cell, I wondered how I came to get here. All I remember is crimson blood dripping off my hands. But that was a long time ago now. I heard the latch go and the door swing open, the light blinding, I was free.

Harriet Fox (12)
Cirencester Kingshill School, Cirencester

Alone

As soon as the siren sounded, I knew it was coming. I had two minutes before it hit. I climbed under the table. I might never see my family again. I might not live. Then it happened, it hit. Now I'm alone, no family, thanks to the Second World War.

Abigail Beasley (12)
Cirencester Kingshill School, Cirencester

147

In Outer Space

In outer space, there is no air, seeing Earth from so far away makes me want to stay here forever. Oh no! It's nearly time to go. At least I can stay here for a bit longer. Still enough time to see the stars. How lovely, bye space, bye stars.

Max Clayton (12)
Cirencester Kingshill School, Cirencester

Boredom In Maths

It's school today and I've got maths! My worst subject. Last time it was algebra, today it's long multiplication, how fun.

The bell rings, lunch is over, maths begins. Boredom. An hour of sleep though is not so bad unless, unless what? Unless that … a supply teacher. This is hell!

Joe Morris (12)
Cirencester Kingshill School, Cirencester

149

Untitled

I held onto him for dear life, so I wouldn't slip and fall
to my death on that cold evil surface.
I let go, suddenly I slipped, my life flashed before me,
my childhood, my adulthood, my wedding, and then
my ice skates slipped.

Spencer Jones (12)
Cirencester Kingshill School, Cirencester

The Manipulative

Four days locked in a house, daylight a memory. Two
good friends dead. One died from starvation, the
other beaten.
Two friends alive together.
'I love you,' speaks the boy.
The girl unlocks the door with her key. 'You said you
loved me.'
The boy fills with rage. He falls …

Liam Coates (14)
Cirencester Kingshill School, Cirencester

Oblivion

'She passed away,'
like storms, swiftly retreating. Like snow, sucked into
oblivion.
'Terribly sorry …'
Numbed chaos, my mind caged, nets of steel,
drawing tight, brittle with memories, searing pain.
Remembrance, mechanically rising frozen fears.
Robotically walking. Her face, her eyes, shuttered.
Her smell. Gone forever, my face cracks. Tears.
Oblivion.

Jenny Hayhurst (13)
Cirencester Kingshill School, Cirencester

The Light

I see a light, shining into my eyes, bright, colourful,
interesting as this light glows into my eyes, as if it
wants something from me. I blink, the light is gone,
I blink again, the light is back, the light starts to flash,
my eyes are concentrating, stop, stare, watch!

Katie Cox (14)
Cirencester Kingshill School, Cirencester

False Paradise

Warming sun, light breeze, fresh air. Relaxation, paradise. The sea's gentle waves washed freely over the expanse of fine, perfect sand, washing away any trace left behind. The bright blue, clear sky allowed the full range of calming light to inhabit the perfect surroundings, but suddenly an explosion. Then, darkness.

Ted Sales (14)
Cirencester Kingshill School, Cirencester

George

There was an old man in front of me. I knew his name 'George,' I said.

The man just said, 'Thank you,' moving his mouth slightly.

That's when I woke up. Just then my cat died. From my bed, I could read 'George' on my cat's name plate.

Ryo Hiruma (13)
Cirencester Kingshill School, Cirencester

Tramp

One day a tramp was walking along the road. A man stopped and talked to him. 'Hello there, you have any money?'
'No I don't I've got no job,' said the tramp.
The young man walked away. He dropped a lottery ticket. The next day the tramp was rich!

Becky Wilson (12)
Cirencester Kingshill School, Cirencester

Then Break Time Came

It was a normal day, in a normal town, on normal Earth. Everything was normal. Then dream time came. It was loud, noisy, pushy and shoving. Break time was no fun anymore. It was boring, unhappy, lonely and sad. Break time was scary. Break time was always dreaded. Everything was normal. Until break time came.

Jessica Williams (12)
Cirencester Kingshill School, Cirencester

A New Day

It was the end of days, no it wasn't, it was the start of a new day, it was cold, the colour leaked out of falling snow. The snow was crispy and crunchy under the new boots, Mom bought for me, right before she died of radiation poisoning.

Ami Uzzeff (12)
Cirencester Kingshill School, Cirencester

In The Jungle

Walking around the jungle, hunting for my prey,
suddenly I head a rustle in the bush. I was panicking,
there was nowhere to hide.
Looking up and down, side to side, hoping it wasn't
a meat-eater as it moved closer and closer. It turned
into a roaring tiger.

Shannon Simpkins
Cirencester Kingshill School, Cirencester

Lost Kitten

It was a nice, sunny day so I let my kitten go outside, I took my eyes off her for two seconds and she disappeared. I looked everywhere, up and down, left and right, she wasn't there. I burst into tears, as it was then I realised she was lost.

Gregory Groome (11)
Cirencester Kingshill School, Cirencester

Death Comes Too Quickly

I was walking along a dark, cold corridor, something caught my eye, moving in front of me, then it vanished. There it was again, I looked for my torch, gone. Something screamed hellishly behind me, I turned around, too late, I was on the floor, dead.

Alexander Kraeter (12)
Downside School, Radstock

Little Red Walking To Granny's House

I was walking, I walked near and far. I walked to and fro along a narrow path, along a road and into the woods. I was followed, I saw a cottage, I knocked, the door opened. 'Granny what big teeth you have.' *Munch* the wolf was tasty.

Alexander Nicholas (11)
Downside School, Radstock

The Airport

At the airport, I was late. I thought I was going to miss my plane, I sprinted, fast as I could. I jumped outside, I saw my plane, I kept my speed. I was so close. There was a pain in my heart. I tripped. The plane ran me over!

Hugo Spink (11)
Downside School, Radstock

The Surprise

I jogged to school, this new big lad got really annoyed at me. I gave him a shove. He hit me in the nose. I got taken to Matron. She helped me. I came out of school, I saw the boy; he was on the roof, he jumped … he died.

William Hoftam (12)
Downside School, Radstock

Gremlins Exist

It was a scary night. I only had a torch. There was a little green creature standing on the road. I realised what it was when it looked up at me with an evil grin on its face. It was a gremlin. It jumped at me - hen I woke up.

Michael Minecki (12)
Downside School, Radstock

Flight 13

Everyone was thrown around. Death seemed certain. Hours ago the plane had taken off, minutes ago it had begun to drop. Minutes of life were left. The captain tried to regain control of the plane and tried to crash-land but they were going too fast. Seconds remained, two, one …

Patrick MacGinnis (11)
Downside School, Radstock

Silence

I glided out over the turquoised water. Not a care in my placid mind. I thought back over the day I had, to the sun-kissed old man, he said 'Beware of sharks.' I did not believe him. Suddenly a flash of white, gaping jaws, then silence, blissful silence.

Ranulph Diggins (11)
Downside School, Radstock

Stolen

'Are you sure?' he shouted.
'Yes, my emerald's gone,' she replied.
The man stepped forward and grabbed something green.
'It was there five minutes ago!' she explained.
'The money?' he asked.
'Gone!' she replied. Something with a green tinge went into his pocket. Then it hit me, he jumped out.

Philip Lowe (12)
Downside School, Radstock

The Feared Sword

Long ago a battle took place between the planets.
Everyone feared the Pleutions because of the deadly
sword their leader clasped in his hands. In the battle
on Earth against Jupiter, the leader died and the
sword was buried. Everyone thought it was a myth
until the sword was found.

Timothy Aspin (12)
Downside School, Radstock

Seconds Later

I threw the frisbee. My dog Rosie chased after it. Suddenly a squeal of brakes, skidding tyres. I raced across the field, praying that nothing had happened to Rosie. A lorry, a man, kneeling on the road. He stood up with Rosie in his arms. 'I'm so sorry,' he whispered.

Elena Kinnersley (12)
Downside School, Radstock

Deep Space

'Pull the lever!'

'I pull that lever, we both die!'

'If we don't drop the cargo and ourselves into space,
no one can put the fire out and it'll blow the ship up!'

'But … '

'Just pull it!' He hesitated, then yanked the lever as
hard as he could. Nothing happened.

Martyn Blakemore (15)
Lakers School, Coleford

171

Being Iſſ

I had a cough and a cold and felt very ill so my friend
took me to the doctors. The doctor told me that I
needed surgery because my heart had exploded.
They finished the surgery and said it was love and
sent me to bed forever in Heaven above.

Laura Wiſſkins (13)
Lakers School, Coleford

Romance On A Train

As I sat down on a train, the boy smiled. Half an hour later, he came to sit by me, we started to chat about what we had in common. I told him, Katie was my name. The train stopped.
We met later under the stars and kissed passionately.

Bernadette Lee (13)
Lakers School, Coleford

173

The Skating Fall

I spun and sped at incredible pace, my dreams and hopes flying into action. The blades spurring up pace, each precise move backed with hours of practice. Down to the last complex sequence, a triple spin, flickering around, but then darkness. Woke up in the hospital.
'You fell,' they said.

Marie-Louise Kertzman (14)
Prior Park College, Bath

Kidnapped

A beautiful day and we go to the park. Talking to another mother while she plays on the swing, her girl comes over to get a drink. I hear a scream! Turning and all I see is an empty swing, swinging slowly my heart stops, then so does the swing.

Katie Pecchia (14)
Prior Park College, Bath

The Lost Cats

'Tabby, teatime!' I shouted. Silence. 'Tabby,' I shouted
again. I asked Beryl if she had seen Tabby. She hadn't
and she couldn't find Tom either! That night I heard
miaowing, I went out to my shed outside and found
out that it was the cats - and fifteen kittens!

Rebecca Aldous (13)
Prior Park College, Bath

Illusion

I walked along the road, pacing. Thinking of anything else possible, but there he was in my head, unmistakably. I walked on hoping it would go away but then I saw him in front of me. *An illusion*, I thought. But no, that was the end.

Abi Everitt (13)
Prior Park College, Bath

Untitled

Autumn weather. I was visiting St Joseph's College; it was years since I was last there. I felt a ghostly presence. I knew that I wasn't alone. Suddenly something ran to the door. I turned to see Mr Bell, a teacher, riding away on his scooter in a comical fashion.

Kentaro Hosoya
St Joseph's Catholic College, Swindon

Crystal Shadows

I never went back to that place again. It was my first visit and my last. The picnic was great until that sinister, paralysing, ghostly tree strangled my dog. I don't know how and I don't know why. Maybe it was the unlucky number as it was my 13th birthday.

Izabella Smolicz (13)
St Joseph's Catholic College, Swindon

Alone

I was alone. Midnight and dreary. I heard a tapping sound from upstairs. I went up and walked over to the attic door that clenched closed. Whispers from inside approached my ear. Then the door flew open, dragged me in. I heard faint words saying 'Help me!'

Shannen Downey (13)
St Joseph's Catholic College, Swindon

The Haunted House

It was midnight with a full moon. The haunted house swayed in the breeze. 'Go in, I dare you,' I whispered.

She walked in through the wrecked door. She started up the stairs, then suddenly the house came crumbling down! She died that day, now her ghost haunts the grounds.

Beth Preston
St Joseph's Catholic College, Swindon

My 50 Word Essay!

Midday. Sgt Smith told us to go over. I was bricking it. 'Men it is your time, go serve our country,' he said calmly.

We all took our rifles and listened to the rest of his speech. I was first over. I looked up, but I would never seen again.

Tom Blackford
St Joseph's Catholic College, Swindon

Untitled

A new boy started school, he wore sunglasses and never took them off.

Two weeks later, he was acting a little weird, we tried to catch him but he was too fast, there one minute, gone the next.

One month later, we caught him, removed his glasses - no eyeballs.

Ryan Townsend (12)
Sandford School, Cheltenham

Once Upon A Wedding

I can't wait for our wedding, it'll be great.
'We are not getting married!'
'I'm not marrying you!'
'Why?'
'Because you are ugly.'
'How can you say that? I had plastic surgery for you!'
'Yes but I told you to have plastic surgery like Twiggy
not Miss Piggy!'
'Oh!'

Ryan Dutson (12)
Sandford School, Cheltenham

Untitled

One day I was sleeping in a tent. At about ten o'clock I heard a scratching noise. I was really scared. I sat there for an hour, terrified, listening to the awful wailing noises. Then a head popped in. 'Come on Bob, you are going to miss the festival bands!'

James Barnes (13)
Sandford School, Cheltenham

Untitled

Me and my mates were staying around Dan's for the week. Every night there was a glowing spot on the wall and it had a picture of someone dying. We didn't know who it was. We focused on the spot and suddenly Billy woke up and said, 'Dan is dead!'

Ryan Wiggins (13)
Sandford School, Cheltenham

Untitled

Jake watched a worm sliding along the earth. The sun glinted on shiny skin highlighting the segments of mottled pink and brown. Jake wondered where the worm was going. Did the worm have a family? Would anyone miss the worm? Then he popped it in his mouth and swallowed - yummy!

Declan James
Sandford School, Cheltenham

187

Untitled

Once there was a boy called Ryan, he had beautiful blue eyes, I loved him so much but I felt like it wasn't working properly so I dumped him one sunny day. The next day I found an engagement ring in my bedroom. I called him but he had gone away.

Leanne Stent (13)
Sandford School, Cheltenham

Casino Gamble

The dealer spread out the cards.
'All in,' I said.
The coloured chips and cards were pushed in … A
trickle of sweat ran down my forehead, this was a
serious gambling experience. A man wearing a suit
looked at me unwillingly,
'All in,' he said, he looked confident. I lost.

William Richardson (12)
Sir Thomas Rich's School, Longlevens

The Phone Goes Dead

'You can contact the dead from this phone, I know,'
said David.
'Look just go to school,' replied Mum.
'Martin! David's bus just crashed, only three people
survived,' yelled Mum.
'Let's use David's phone to phone the school,'
answered Dad worriedly.
Their number is 1541234566.
'Hello.'
'Hi it's David …'

Haamed Al Hassan
Sir Thomas Rich's School, Longlevens

190

If Only There Was Someone To Live For

The bang of a thousand soldiers marched to their destination. *Us!* As I stared at the men coming over the horizon, people behind rushed around snatching any provisions they could before swinging onto horses and riding away. I could've followed but I stayed. I had nobody to live for.

Chris Brook (13)
Sir Thomas Rich's School, Longlevens

My Last Moments

My heart fluttered as the blow fell. I fell to my knees breathing in bursts. My ears whistling, all other sounds obsolete, sight blurring.
The figure stood over me, its outline fuzzy as tears invaded my eyes. My ears cleared and gave way to the final cries of my heart.

James Drinkwater (13)
Sir Thomas Rich's School, Longlevens

The Voices

I ran away from the terror of the voices. 'Am I
laughing? You're not funny, sit down!'
So I sat down and cried, till my eyes started to hurt.
It was a very bad day, very bad!

Jack Goodwin (13)
Sir Thomas Rich's School, Longlevens

The Splattered Light

The light, glimmering, it shoots into my eyes as if a bullet. I peer past the broken, rickety mirror and ponder at the view I see. Blood and guts had been splattered onto the walls, what happened here? Suddenly I felt a spear point in my back. Failure.

Christian Swift (13)
Sir Thomas Rich's School, Longlevens

Bullying

The gang close in. Fists fly towards me. The sun shines down on the sweat on my head, my hands spring up to protect my face. Friends encourage friends, teachers yell, whistles scream. Girls shout, blood, cold, red, dark blood runs down my scarred and humiliated face. It is over.

Rhys Davies (13)
Sir Thomas Rich's School, Longlevens

An Evil Demon Or A Chav?

I pulled the sword from it's sheath, my hands trembling, I thrust the sword into the evil Delrith, just as Gypsy Aris told me. The body of the demon fell to the floor and decomposed in an instant. It had turned into acid. Then I knew it was a chav!

Adam Williams (13)
Sir Thomas Rich's School, Longlevens

The Game

The noise coming out of the tunnel was like thunder through your ears. The atmosphere in the high-tech 400 million stadium felt like the world was filling the stands. The light from the floodlights blinded your eyes. The kit on me felt like golden cotton, I felt like I billion.

Luke Burford (11)

Sir Thomas Rich's School, Longlevens

The Chase

I hit the fuse. There was an explosion and I was out.
Racing down a country lane on a motorbike, bullets
racing past my face. I skidded under a crate and ran
to my car, I had escaped, speeding down a country
lane. There was a loud bang. Then black.

George Schreuder (12)
Sir Thomas Rich's School, Longlevens

Fighting With Stars

Bang! Danny shuddered as the torpedo hit his interceptor class starship. 'I'm taking heavy fire!' he shouted into his radio, hoping Federal Command would pick him up and send help. A flashing red siren told him all armour was depleted. Now only his hull protected him from steaming laser beams.

Toby Churchley (11)
Sir Thomas Rich's School, Longlevens

Mr Bean's Holiday

'Noooo!' I screamed as my father went in the right train while I was on the wrong one. I came across a British tourist. Man he was dumb. Tripping over stuff etc. He offered to help find my parents by ringing every number in France. But we never found 'em.

Numair Moosa (12)
Sir Thomas Rich's School, Longlevens

The Matrix

Hacking was a lengthy process so I was nearly asleep by the time the green-tinged words flashed up. I just couldn't believe that all my hopes rested on this one woman. The bullets were nothing. They were just objects. I had control of everything, I was the chosen one.

Sam Westwood (12)

Sir Thomas Rich's School, Longlevens

The House

I entered the deep, dark house, creeping past ancient paintings and suits of armour that seemed to be moving. I creaked open a cupboard and a corpse crashed down to the floor, accompanied by a swarm of bats, which knocked me off my feet. I slowly crept forward, into nothingness.

Edward Burgess (11)
Sir Thomas Rich's School, Longlevens

202

The Robbery

Shadows crept along the walls. A ghostly screaming sounded nearby. I heard a crash of glass and the bleep of the alarm. I crept along the walls to the trophy room. A man with a gun was in the room. He fired at the lights and the room went dark.

Oliver Roper (12)

Sir Thomas Rich's School, Longlevens

203

Sweat

Jack looked over his shoulder, he was still being chased. Cold sweat trickled down his neck, his pursuers were invincible. Jack ran into a dead end, a sheer drop to the motorway below. Jack launched himself onto the roof of a passing truck and gestured rudely at his pursuers.

Chris Murphy (12)
Sir Thomas Rich's School, Longlevens

When The Snake Strikes

Standing still, he watched the snake getting closer and closer. He knew that if he moved, he would die. Suddenly he noticed a spider abseiling down his field of vision. It landed on his face and crawled onto his nose. He sneezed, the snake struck, he died in the dark.

James Stokes (11)
Sir Thomas Rich's School, Longlevens

Him

I took another tiny step down the alleyway, even though the street was just behind me, I felt alone. The moonlight glinted off the bin. What was that? A noise, a movement then suddenly something grabbed me by the arm. I let out a tiny scream, I saw the tiniest …

Joe Cusworth (13)
Sir Thomas Rich's School, Longlevens

Black World

A flash of blades and an explosion. I fell, landing on my knees. The world went black, black turned to blue and white and I woke up in a jungle full of armed gunmen. Behind me was a burning boulder and a cliff. A shot. My arm stung. An ambush.

Jack Blackwell (11)
The Cotswold School, Cheltenham

The Little Red Man

A little red man was in his bath when his doorbell
went. He put on his towel and answered it.
'Hello?' suddenly his towel fell down.
The little yellow lady, who was crossing the road,
stopped and was run down.
Moral: Never cross the road when the red man's
flashing!

Caffum Hasefer (12)
The Cotswold School, Cheltenham

Night Fright

Click, click, click, creak … click, click, click, click.
I felt the blanket being tweezed from my shaking hands.
I peered over the edge into the pitiless, evil eyes before me.
I shivered and quaked.
'Did old grandpa's walking stick scare you me boy?'

Matthew Twin (12)
The Cotswold School, Cheltenham

Woofers

The girl could feel its breath down her neck. Its dark fur was tickling her chin. Its brown eyes glowed in the moon's light. She could hear it snuffling around her feet. Then her mum came out the house and she was calling it. 'Woofers, Woofers time to come in.'

Effie Bowen (12)
The Cotswold School, Cheltenham

Pirates!

The boat swayed as I stood on it. I put my pirate hat
on and shouted, 'Oooharrh!'
My crew were in front of me, working hard. I was
the captain of my ship! Suddenly I heard a noise.
Argh, a monster.
'Run,' I shouted.
'Kids stop playing, time for tea!'

Jade Ennis (13)
The Cotswold School, Cheltenham

The Chase

I ran through the forest ducking under branches.
I could hear his feet pounding in the background.
I saw my friend running beside me, he turned and
disappeared. I knew my pursuer would get me, I
knew there was no point. I stopped.
'Tag! You're it!'
The chase began again.

Rhys Powell (13)
The Cotswold School, Cheltenham

Trapped

A room of no doors. A room of no escape. A slither of slime and a hiss of smoke. There was no way in, no way out. I looked from side to side, top to bottom. A sharp, blinding light piercing the dark surroundings.

'One less spider!'

Alexander Karkfins (13)

The Cotswold School, Cheltenham

Murder!

Jack stepped into the deserted street.
'Hello Chris Williams,'
'I'm not Chris Williams, he's wanted for murder!'
The gun cocked.
'Please, I'm not him!'
Bang!
The murderer dumped the body into the river.
'I know you're not Chris Williams,' he sneered in a
quiet whisper, 'cos I am.'

Joseph Armstrong (13)
The Cotswold School, Cheltenham

214

The Ghost In The Garden

Terror! The shed goes to the ground, spades thrown.
Moving closer to the window. *Smash!* Glass breaks.
It wants me, reason's unknown. It's coming in closer.
Through the door. Face to face. Dark eyes, dark face,
dark everything, *bang!* It got me. Fair and square.

Tom Morsey (12)

The John Bentley School, Calne

There It Was

There it was, right in front of me. It was going to happen. I struggled but under all this rubble, I had no chance. After the bombing I knew I was a goner. I could hear them searching, I hoped, I shook with dreaded fear but would I be found?

Daniel Turk (12)
The John Bentley School, Calne

The House Of No Return

The house was spooky and scary. Eyes were watching me from all sides. I heard a scream and ran for the door but it wouldn't open. I shouted, I bellowed but no one could hear me. I saw a window but it slammed shut. I sat there alone that night.

Luke Curnock (13)
The John Bentley School, Calne

The Punch

Drawing back for the strike, when the fist came flying. The rock hard knuckles shining pale. When the fist came flying, from the blow, I hit the floor, because the fist came flying.

Daniel Bailey (13)
The John Bentley School, Calne

Journey Home

The school bell rings, everyone rushes out the school doors, it's manic as I make my way to my bus, it's hammering with rain and I finally get on the bus. The bus engine starts up with a shudder, as we start to move, and make the journey home.

Chloe Willcocks (13)

The John Bentley School, Calne

Untitled

Then the rain came, I ran, they came, I ran and ran. *Bang!* I dived, I hit my head then nothing, I tried to get up but it was useless. They came and came, it came, then nothing. I was filled with fear, it came *for me!*

Graham Beff (13)
The John Bentley School, Calne

That Night

That very night, moonlight gently shining through the window. Wind lightly whistling in my ears, it's freaking me out. Huddled under my duvet that now feels hard and lumpy. I run down the stairs, frightened, I can't find my parents. Then I see them. With a scream I wake up.

Harriet Cunningham (13)
The John Bentley School, Calne

Untitled

Sitting there, hopelessly knowing there's nothing I can do.
Waiting for the nurse to come and tell me the bad news, like something had gone wrong in the operation, that there was nothing they could do, then tell me it wasn't my fault but deep inside, I knew it was.

Hannah Peirce (13)
The John Bentley School, Calne

The Graveyard

As I walk through the graveyard, there's silence. Moonlight shining down upon me, fog hanging in the air. I can feel the cold, jagged wind against my face. I'm not alone. I hear whatever it is coming closer, closer, closer, it lets out a high-pitched scream, it's too late.

Joe Makepeace (13)
The John Bentley School, Calne

223

The Road To Wembley

I remembered the great game against Blackburn.
The dramatic winners. I remembered the tension
between the two fans. Terry had done it, he had let
us through to the Cup Final, this was our year.

Connor Lennon (12)
The John Bentley School, Calne

224

Matty And The Cricket Match

I walked across the wicket, I knew I would bowl well. I was ready. The open batsman was in, I was confident that this was my day. The first ball drifted through the air, the batsman smashed it for six. The next one was a wide,
curse the stupid horoscope!

Connor Rafferty (12)
The John Bentley School, Calne

What's Happening In The World?

I sit on top of the disgusting world watching terrible things happen - rubbish, bullying, smoking, racism, why do we do things like it? Is it just for fun or do we mean it? Why? That's why I cry to the bad world. What people why?

Ashley Riff (12)
The John Bentley School, Calne

226

The Chase

Padding feet, open mouth, grey and white creeping
fast, stalking a deer. Shadow pouncing, deer fleeing,
the chase is on. Brown galloping faster than wind,
panting creature behind catching up, deer slowing.
Creature pounding. Flying brown animal, crying wolf,
wolf throwing himself in front of deer.
'Can we be friends?'

Kayleigh Scrivens (11)
The John Bentley School, Calne

Who Ate The Sweets?

'Did you eat the sweets Meg?'
'No I didn't!' but she smirked as if she had.
She had eaten the sweets but she didn't want to tell
her mum because she knew she would get
told off.
She told her mum who had a go at her and grounded
her!

Abby Carter (12)
The John Bentley School, Calne

The Beach

We went to the beach, me, my mum, dad oh and baby Ben. I felt the sand between my toes but suddenly *ouch!* I fell through a hole, my leg bent awkwardly, now it's in plaster. Can't wait to tell everyone at school. *Ouch*, the problem is it really hurts!

Shona Harding (12)
The John Bentley School, Calne

Sat On A Cloud

I sat on a cloud, watching the people fight for what
they believe. I saw five men tortured just like I was
and I felt powerless. I wanted to help but I couldn't
as I was not there. I was slowly fading away as I
watched the battle be lost.

Rachel Bate (11)
The John Bentley School, Calne

230

Slain

He ran down the corridor avoiding the fire blown by
the ferocious dragon. Jumping into the sky he struck
with no luck. Quickly he jumped for a weak pillar
pushing with all his might. It fell whacking the dragon
on the head. It stumbled into the lava. Slowly dying.

Christian Plumb (12)
The John Bentley School, Calne

231

Story Writing In 50 Words Or Less

A child in school was asked to write a story in 50 words or less, he had no idea what to write so he just wrote about himself and what he was doing. It started with '*A child in school was asked to write a story in 50 words or …*'

Jack Reeves (12)

The John Bentley School, Calne

One Dark Corner

I walked through the sunny streets, I saw joy and smiles all around. Laughter filled the busy town and all I could do was smile. But as the dark corners approached I saw rubbish everywhere, people being mugged, racism, swearing, everything bad in the world. All in one dark corner.

Jodie Hoskin (12)
The John Bentley School, Calne

Lost Boy

One day a boy named Tom went out for a walk with his mum. She said he could go off for a bit but be back soon. Tom went down the path and then found himself in a deep, dark forest. Where was he? What would happen to poor Tom?

Lauren West (12)
The John Bentley School, Calne

234

Sleepy Dog

There was a dog called Patch, he couldn't sleep so he climbed up a tree. It still didn't work, so he barked to make the noise stop. That didn't work so he ran into the shed. *That's better* he thought, he fell asleep in a flowerpot. Goodnight Patch.

Celeste Bunton (11)
The John Bentley School, Calne

Unlucky

Another day, another detention. Guess what happened this time? I blew up the science lab! Just because I was staring at Ffion, her eyes … anyway, so I blew up the science lab. No big deal. Two weeks detention. Sigh.
Guess what? My luck has changed. Ffion fancies me!

Mef Hargreaves (12)
The John Bentley School, Calne

Whooo!

A woman was really annoyed with her husband because he went to the pub every night, claiming he saw a ghost. She followed him that night dressed as a ghost, crept up behind him and said 'Whooo!' He said, 'Argh!'
'So you've brought a friend Ghost?'
She heard something, *'Whooo!'*

Lauren Henry (11)
The John Bentley School, Calne

On The Beach

I feel the sand between my toes, watching the waves ripple back and forth. The sun beating down and the palm trees swaying in the breeze. On the beach I feel out of place as girls walk by with their bikinis and perfect tans. Why can't I be like them?

Lucinda Lowe (12)
The John Bentley School, Calne

Evil Or Friendly?

The bear's fur was rough and strangled. He had eyes
of death and his claws were like blades. His mane
was dull with bits of what looked like blood. His eyes
turned at me and my blood stopped running.
'Roar!'
Was he friend or evil?
I was about to know.

Brett Perrett (11)
The John Bentley School, Calne

239

Punching The Problem

She was nice at first. We shared a dorm but she always broke the rules. She put on ear-piercing music. I asked her to turn it down; she turned it up. It was snowing. I asked her to close the window, she opened it more. I punched her.

Maddie Moxey (12)
The John Bentley School, Calne

Run And Cover

Bullets speeding over my head. People slumping to the ground all around me. The noise of gunfire echoing around my skull. My brother (half-hidden behind a sandbag wall) encouraging me, but in a split second, the wall is gone and him with it. A sacrifice of war!

George Bishop (11)
The John Bentley School, Calne

Untitled

Silence crept through the bedroom, along with a thief.
Driinngg cried the burglar alarm, up got Dad, grabbed a tennis racket, ran down the landing, downstairs only to find a knocked down kitchen bin and the neighbour's cat carrying leftover bacon.
'Oh not again?' groaned Dad and went upstairs.

Danielle Donovan (12)
The John Bentley School, Calne

242

Little Boy, Little Boy

Once upon a time, there lived a boy who was seven years old. He loved toys, sadly his family were very poor so they could only afford one a year. Just around the corner there was a sweet shop and he loved looking through the window at the tempting sweets!

Jessica Want (12)
The John Bentley School, Calne

School

One day a boy got a note to go to a magical school far away. The boy accepted it. Five days later, he was on his way. To get there you had to go across a lake. He found it scary. He opened the door to find it was closed!

Josh Fry (13)
The John Bentley School, Calne

The Drag Car

Here I was sat in the car, waiting for the lights to go green, they went, throttle to the floor, I was winning the race until it happened. The front tyre blew and the car rolled and rolled, that was it, everything went black, I thought I would die.

Ashley Smith (13)
The John Bentley School, Calne

Untitled

I walked the long corridor down the tunnel onto the pitch with the three lions on my shirt, next to my pounding heart. The crowd stood and applauded me. Suddenly the alarm buzzes and my eyes open to a dark room.
My bedroom.

Jack Haines (13)
The John Bentley School, Calne

Boldylocks And The 3 Bears

'It wasn't me!' cried Baby Bear.
'Well it must've been the magic fairy again then!'
Daddy Bear groaned, 'I suppose chairs snap
themselves then?'
Daddy Bear took him upstairs to bed and found
Boldylocks lying in the bed! Boldylocks jumped up
and ran away. Daddy Bear fainted, breaking the bed!

Maisie Manfield (12)

Worle School, Weston-Super-Mare

The Bar

A man walked into a bar. He coughed from all the smoke. Men were drinking. Women were dancing. He walked up to the bar and demanded service. He sat on the stool. The bar man asked 'Yes?' The man replied, 'One pint please!' Eventually he got his beloved pint.

Jessica Collins (13)
Worle School, Weston-Super-Mare

Sweeping Shadow Of The Night

It sweeps the ground in the silence of the night. I turn around startled, but there is no one there, I carry on walking but I can see looming shapes and distant footsteps. I turn again, there's nothing there. Just my shadow statue-like and motionless and time stands still.

Josephine Compitus (13)
Worle School, Weston-Super-Mare

Secret Friend

I have a best friend. He's called Bob. People say he's my imaginary friend but he's not. I can see him. He's right here. Can't you see him too?
Ten years later, Bob is still here, but I don't tell anyone about him. He's my secret friend, no one else's.

Heather Buchanan-Glew (13)
Worle School, Weston-Super-Mare

The Horse, The Girl

Quietly Horse clambers by, hooves bashing, head not high, tail scruffy, eyes sad, mane on neck, tangled, mad. But Girl, she's sad too, hair tangled, cries too, through unhappiness and sadness they meet. No longer Horse clambers by, no longer Girl cries, Girl and family see Horse is now family.

Lauren Green (13)
Worle School, Weston-Super-Mare

M

We all share the thought of murder rushing through our heads. Whether you want to kill someone or have done, it's always on our mind. Murder can come from love, anger, depression, emotions are reasons for murder. I knew she was there, I just wish I could have stopped him.

Daniel Cross (13)
Worle School, Weston-Super-Mare

The Battle

He was confident, he clenched the handle and pulled the sword, it slid gracefully out of its sheath with an ominous *shhh* …. He walked forward towards his enemy. *Then* his arrogant swagger faltered, he collapsed to the floor, a crimson-red stain blossomed from the arrow wound on his chest.

Thomas Clark (13)
Worle School, Weston-Super-Mare

253

The World Cup Final

It was the World Cup Final and a cracking game,
all the other games were lame, last minute and the
score was three all, until someone fouled me and I
took a fall. I curled the free kick as the goal looked
smaller, the ball swerved into the top corner.

Matt Harding (13)
Worle School, Weston-Super-Mare

The Bird

There is a legendary bird of prey, it eats 20 mice a day, it smells of ashes when you see it, it dashes. It once bit off a man's arm, it was frightened so it harmed. This is a legendary bird of prey. Beware it will get you one day.

Troy Hannam (13)
Worle School, Weston-Super-Mare

Shiny Stars

When I'm all on my own, all sad, I look out of my window at the stars because friends are like stars, always there for you. Boys are like buses, they come and go every five minutes so when your heart is in pieces, always look at the shiny stars.

Caroline Bify (13)
Worle School, Weston-Super-Mare

Goodnight My Friend

So you have finally come to the gates then, were you in trouble with some sickening men? Did you have a life-threatening disease or were you in a crash and your body is debris? Why are you here then? Have you been used?
No Sir, I've been racially abused.

Cameron Francis (13)
Worle School, Weston-Super-Mare

Black Shadow

A dark black shadow is right there beside me but no one is there. Everywhere I go it follows me silently. It's starting to freak me out though. I told my mum about this shadow that follows me. She said it was my own shadow - no one else's - it's mine!

Saskia Eager (13)
Worle School, Weston-Super-Mare

Midnight Scare!

I woke up, midnight, what's that? A noise over at the
window! And a shadow. I hide under the sheets of
my bed, I was scared stiff! I couldn't move! Eventually
I plucked up the courage to go and see what it was.
A tree! How silly can you get?

Benjamin Gutsell (13)
Worle School, Weston-Super-Mare

Danny Donkey

Danny went and one day saw his friend Owl. They found a hole full of Polos, biscuits, Smarties and even Rolos.
'*Mmm* yummy,' said Danny.
In a flash it was all gone.
'Come on, let's go,' but what was this? - he was stuck in the hole!

Caroline Higgins (13)
Worle School, Weston-Super-Mare

260

The Dog

There is a dog named Tim who roams the streets. Each day he looks for food in bins. He likes to bark at people with walking sticks. He loves to rip things up but most of all he would love a nice, caring family to look after and love him.

Jade Hopkins (12)
Worle School, Weston-Super-Mare

The Fat Cat

Tom crept through the dark passage and into a quiet room. The room full of people looked shocked. They all started to whisper to each other. Tom looked at Jade with such an innocent and disappointed look. One person in the room said, 'Jade your cat's got fat hasn't he?'

Shayne Hoddinott (13)
Worle School, Weston-Super-Mare

The Last Noise

The guns boomed above their heads. The rain poured down, they stared across no-man's-land, the watch still ticking. The mud covered everyone but no one cared. A bomb landed. Three gone, four, five. The watch still ticked. Then nothing. Silence, the watch ticked no more. They were dead.

Hannah Connelly (13)

Worle School, Weston-Super-Mare

Butterfly

He stood by the window with it wide open. The wind was a light breeze. The sun shone. He could fly, like the butterfly outside. He could, he could. He jumped, he was doing it! He reached the floor. Not a butterfly, a broken-dreamed boy. There was silence.

Jessica Durant (13)
Worle School, Weston-Super-Mare

Untitled

I saw something move in the dark room. I walked in, I felt a breeze. I looked at the figure. All of a sudden, it jumped up and was holding a pair of scissors, it whispered, 'Get a fashion sense.' There was a flash of light and she was gone.

Lucy Cooling (13)
Worle School, Weston-Super-Mare

Football

A man bought a football, he was good. He played for England and Villa, when he played, the sunlight bounced off the ball and made it gleam. The crowd cheered as he shot and scored. The whole crowd were on their feet. As full-time came, he walked off happily.

Matthew Bradley-Tyler (13)
Worle School, Weston-Super-Mare

266

The Man

The night moonlight hit me in the eye, I opened the door to a man. Was he slim or fat? Was he short or tall? Was his hair long or short? Were his shoes red or blue or yellow? Was it a man or was it all just a dream?

Jack Book (13)
Worle School, Weston-Super-Mare

The Dark Room

The dark room filled me with suspense and wonder. It looked interesting and dangerous. Welcoming and chilling, right down to the bone. I longed to walk in but run away at the same time. I wanted to laugh loudly and cry. I switched the light on and it was gone.

Sophie Bishop-Hurman (13)
Worle School, Weston-Super-Mare

The Crafty Cat

He lies in wait till everyone's asleep, so that he can smuggle away the goods. There's a cake on the window sill and he plans to steal it. The window's open, he climbs in and tucks into the double chocolate cake. Someone walks in and he shoots out the window.

Janet Jones (12)
Worle School, Weston-Super-Mare

Scarred For Life

'I want faster,' I yelled to Gemma.
'Faster is what you will get,' she replied whilst
gathering up her strength. 'Heave.'
There I was gliding through the air like an angel but
it ended with a heavy landing that left me scarred for
life. What a painful experience I had.

Natasha Foster (12)
Worle School, Weston-Super-Mare

Crashing Into The Fence

2 months ago, me and Gareth went to Ashcombe Park on our bikes to ride down the hills. The only problem was the grass was very slippery. I went down first and it took me 30 feet to stop before the fence.
Gareth whizzed down and straight into the fence!

Ashley Cox (12)
Worle School, Weston-Super-Mare

Ouch That Hurt!

I was on the trampoline. I was going really high, then Mum came out and said, 'Be careful, don't go too high.'
'I won't,' I yelled back. Suddenly I fell off the trampoline! It felt like ages before I smacked against the ground. 'Ouch that hurt!' I cried in pain.

Natasha Bendall (12)
Worle School, Weston-Super-Mare

Hidden Go Hit

'60, ready or not, here I come!' Geoff shouted. David ran inside to search for a place to hide. David waited ten minutes and decided to go out and see where Geoff was. David ran outside and found Geoff passed out. He suddenly saw a figure run around the corner.

Jay Harris (12)

Worle School, Weston-Super-Mare

The Day I Broke A Leg

Rushing down the stairs, my sister was chasing me. 'Ouch my knee,' she had pushed me. A bone was sticking out my leg. Mum put me in the car and scurried me to hospital. Nurse said I had to put it in plaster to heal for a few weeks.

Courtney Wilson (12)
Worle School, Weston-Super-Mare

A Blast With A Splash

'Oh you're so dead,' screamed my friend Nicole.
'I don't think so,' I said, pouring another bucket of
water over her.
I ran down her road to her house and her dad came
running out but Nicole splashed her dad with the
bucket she was trying to get me with.

Hannah-Marie Martin (12)
Worle School, Weston-Super-Mare

Get You

My brother shouting at me, 'I'm going to get you.'
'No you're not,' I shouted.
My brother had his water pistol. I was running
around the garden with my football. I threw the
football at him, he didn't see it. It hit him in the face
and he passed out.

Aimee Leppard (12)
Worle School, Weston-Super-Mare

Information

We hope you have enjoyed reading this book - and that you will continue to enjoy it in the coming years.

If you like reading and writing, drop us a line or give us a call and we'll send you a free information pack. Alternatively visit our website at www.youngwriters.co.uk

Write to:
Young Writers Information,
Remus House,
Coltsfoot Drive,
Peterborough,
PE2 9JX
Tel: (01733) 890066
Email: youngwriters@forwardpress.co.uk